Bond

Verbal Reasoning

Assessment Papers

8–9 years

J M Bond

Nelson Thornes

First published in 2002 by:
Nelson Thornes Ltd

This edition published in 2011 by:
Nelson Thornes Ltd
Delta Place
27 Bath Road
CHELTENHAM
GL53 7TH
United Kingdom

13 14 / 10 9 8 7 6 5 4 3 2

A catalogue record for this book is available from the British Library

ISBN 978 1 4085 1696 6

Page make-up by Tech Set Ltd

Printed in China by 1010 Printing International Ltd

Before you get started

What is Bond?

This book is part of the Bond Assessment Papers series for verbal reasoning, which provides a **thorough and continuous course in verbal reasoning** from ages six to twelve. It builds up verbal reasoning skills from book to book over the course of the series.

What does this book cover?

Verbal reasoning questions can be grouped into four distinct groups: sorting words, selecting words, anagrams, coded sequences and logic. This book practises a wide range of questions appropriate to the age group drawn from all these categories. One of the key features of Bond Assessment Papers is that each one practises **a very wide variety of skills and question types** so that children are always challenged to think – and don't get bored repeating the same question type again and again. We believe that variety is the key to effective learning. It helps children 'think on their feet' and cope with the unexpected.

The age given on the cover is for guidance only. As the papers are designed to be reasonably challenging for the age group, any one child may naturally find him or herself working above or below the stated age. The important thing is that children are always encouraged by their performance. Working at the right level is the key to this.

What does the book contain?

- **20 papers** – each one contains 45 questions.
- **Scoring devices** – there are score boxes next to the questions and a Progress Chart at the back. The chart is a visual and motivating way for children to see how they are doing. Encouraging them to colour in the chart as they go along and to try to beat their last score can be highly effective!
- **Next Steps** – advice on what to do after finishing the papers can be found on the inside back cover.
- **Answers** – located in an easily-removed central pull-out section.

How can you use this book?

One of the great strengths of Bond Assessment Papers is their flexibility. They can be used at home, school and by tutors to:

- provide regular verbal reasoning practice in **bite-sized chunks**
- **highlight strengths and weaknesses** in the core skills
- identify **individual needs**
- set **homework**
- set **timed formal practice tests** – allow about 30 minutes.

It is best to start at the beginning and work through the papers in order.

What does a score mean and how can it be improved?

If children colour in the Progress Chart at the back, this will give an idea of how they are doing. The Next Steps inside the back cover will help you to decide what to do next to help a child progress. We suggest that it is always valuable to go over any wrong answers with children.

Don't forget the website...!

Visit www.bond11plus.co.uk for lots of advice, information and suggestions on everything to do with Bond, helping children to do their best, and exams.

Paper 1

Underline the pair of words most similar in meaning.

Example   come, go   <u>roam, wander</u>   fear, fare

1   <u>alley, lane</u>   real, false   back, forward

2   good, bad   bake, oven   <u>heavy, weighty</u>

3   beat, lose   <u>bite, nip</u>   bath, room

4   nose, face   shallow, river   <u>correct, right</u>

5   <u>come, go</u>   sorry, glad   <u>closed, shut</u>

5

Find the three-letter word which can be added to the letters in capitals to make a new word. The new word will complete the sentence sensibly.

Example   The cat sprang onto the MO.   <u>USE</u>

6   SN days make a week.   EVE

7   We put SS on our feet.   HOE

8   He FED his cup.   ILL

9   They SED me the way to the town.   HOW

10   I would like to hear a story BEE I go to sleep.   For

5

Underline two words, one from each group, that go together to form a new word. The word in the first group always comes first.

Example   (hand, <u>green</u>, for)   (light, <u>house</u>, sure)

11   (is, <u>be</u>, it)   (bed, <u>low</u>, high)

12   (shut, open, <u>in</u>)   (<u>side</u>, back, air)

13   (<u>for</u>, form, fear)   (car, <u>got</u>, back)

14   (toe, <u>finger</u>, hand)   (rip, <u>tip</u>, side)

15   (<u>face</u>, hair, hand)   (shave, <u>some</u>, were)

5

Change the first word of the third pair in the same way as the other pairs to give a new word.

Example   bind, hind   bare, hare   but, <u>hut</u>

16 art, part   ale, pale   ant, <u>pant</u>

17 ill, till   all, tall   ear, <u>tear</u>

18 pick, prick   feed, freed   tied, <u>tried</u>

19 ran, rain   man, main   pan <u>pain</u>

20 top, stop   tar, star   tab, <u>stab</u>

5

Fill in the missing letters. The alphabet has been written out to help you.

A B C D E F G H I J K L M N O P Q R S T U V W X Y Z

Example   A B is to C D as P Q is to <u>R S</u>

21 A is to D as G is to   <u>J</u>

22 3B is to 4D as 5F is to <u>6H</u>

23 ABD is to BCE as CDF is to <u>DEG</u>

24 MAB is to NBC as OCD is to <u>PDE</u>

25 9AB is to 8CD as 7EF is to <u>6GH</u>

5

Fill in the crosswords so that all the given words are included. You have been given one letter as a clue in each crossword.

26

27

H	O	M	E
I	■	■	D
N	■	■	I
T	E	N	T

edit, hint, home, tent

T	E	R	M
I	■	■	O
M	■	■	S
E	N	D	S

ends, moss, term, time

28

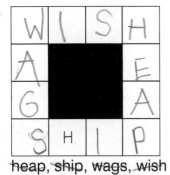

W	I	S	H
A	■	■	E
G	■	■	A
S	H	I	P

heap, ship, wags, wish

3

Fill in the missing number in each sequence.

Example 2 4 6 8 _10_

29 12   15   _18_   21   24

30 1996   1998   _2000_   2002   2004

31 20   17   14   11   _8_

32 4.5   5.0   5.5   6.0   _6.5_

33 17   _20_   23   26   29

34 20   18   15   11   _6_

6

13579

If the code for PEARS is 13579, what are the codes for the following words?

35 ARE _573_   36 RAP _751_

37 SPA _975_   38 SEE _933_

39 PEA _135_

What do these codes stands for?

40 91357 _SPEAR_   41 511357 _APPEAR_

7

Here are some TV programmes.

> 14:00 Play School
>
> 14:15 Cartoons
>
> 15:30 Think Twice
>
> 16:00 The School on the Hill
>
> 16:30 News

How many minutes do these programmes last?

42 Play School _15_ minutes   43 Cartoons _15_ minutes

44 Think Twice _30_ minutes   45 The School on the Hill _30_ minutes

4

Paper 2

Underline the word in brackets closest in meaning to the word in capitals.

Example   UNHAPPY (unkind death laughter <u>sad</u> friendly)

1 CLEVER   (school <u>bright</u> pupil stupid trick)

2 QUICK   (slow <u>fast</u> speed walk step)

3 LAUGH   (cry taught funny <u>chuckle</u> humour)

4 MODERN   (easy today young <u>new</u> trend)

5 SIMPLE   (crazy silly hard <u>easy</u> straight)

5

Complete the following sentences in the best way by choosing one word from each set of brackets.

Example   Tall is to (tree, <u>short</u>, colour) as narrow is to (thin, white, <u>wide</u>).

6 Top is to (<u>bottom</u>, pot, over) as fat is to (side, <u>thin</u>, chubby).

7 Fair is to (fear, <u>dark</u>, shop) as clean is to (wash, <u>dirty</u>, soap).

8 Short is to (fat, thin, <u>tall</u>) as lost is to (win, one, <u>found</u>).

9 Full is to (<u>empty</u>, over, cup) as rough is to (tumble, cross, <u>smooth</u>).

10 Shut is to (<u>open</u>, close, key) as fast is to (<u>slow</u>, speed, late).

5

Find the letter which will end the first word and start the second word.

Example   peac (<u>h</u>) ome

11 han (<u>d</u>) oor

12 mat (<u>e</u>) ver

13 sal (<u>t</u>) ill

14 duc (<u>k</u>) ite

15 mas (<u>t</u>) est

5

4

Fill in the crosswords so that all the given words are included. You have been given one letter as a clue in each crossword.

16

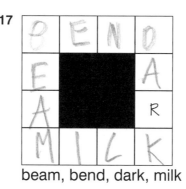

C	A	M	P
A	■	■	L
T	■	■	U
S	H	A	M

cats, camp, plum, sham

17

P	E	N	D
E	■	■	A
A	■	■	R
M	I	L	K

beam, bend, dark, milk

18

B	A	N	K
E	■	■	I
A	■	■	N
R	I	N	G

bank, bear, king, ring

○ 3

Underline two words, one from each group, that go together to form a new word. The word in the first group always comes first.

Example (hand, <u>green</u>, for) (light, <u>house</u>, sure)

19 (<u>bed</u>, for, right) (tub, cot, <u>side</u>)

20 (near, after, <u>under</u>) (some, <u>ground</u>, set)

21 (in, <u>an</u>, it) (left, <u>form</u>, just)

22 (far, <u>near</u>, out) (law, police, <u>here</u>)

23 (<u>far</u>, for, ran) (take, give, <u>us</u>)

○ 5

Change the first word into the last word by changing one letter at a time and making a new word in the middle.

Example CASE *CASH* LASH

24 PANE PINE PINK

25 COMB COME HOME

○ 5

26 HOPE _COPE_ COPY

27 HATE _MATE_ MITE

28 COLD _GOLD_ GILD

If the code for POSTER is 235689, what are the codes for the following words?

29 STOP _5632_   30 SET _586_

What do these codes stand for?

31 632 _TOP_   32 6355 _TOSS_

33 899 _ERR_

Choose the word or phrase that makes each sentence true.

Example   A LIBRARY always has (posters, a carpet, <u>books</u>, DVDs, stairs).

34 A HOUSE always has (a garage, curtains, <u>walls</u>, a doorbell, a fence).

35 A LAKE always has (ducks, boats, fish, swans, <u>water</u>).

36 A CITY always has (farms, <u>buildings</u>, an airport, an underground, a river).

37 A KITCHEN always has (a table, chairs, <u>a stove</u>, plants, a radio).

38 A SCHOOL always has (a cafeteria, a nurse, <u>students</u>, a swimming pool, a bus).

Underline the two words which are made from the same letters.

Example   TAP   PET   <u>TEA</u>   POT   <u>EAT</u>

39 MEAT   TIME   TUNE   TEAM   MUST

40 NUT   TEN   NET   TAN   NOT

41 TEST   STAB   LAST   LOST   SALT

6

Remove one letter from the word in capitals to leave a new word.
The meaning of the new word is given in the clue.

Example A U N T   an insect   _ant_

42 FARM   not near   _far_

43 HARM   a piece of meat   _ham_

44 GROUND   shaped like a ball   _round_

45 THAN   you get it from sunbathing _tan_

4

Now go to the Progress Chart to record your score!   Total   45

Paper 3

Underline the two words which are the odd ones out in the following groups of words.

Example   black   <u>king</u>   purple   green   <u>house</u>

1 noisy   peaceful   <u>crowd</u>   calm   <u>concert</u>

2 small   short   <u>enlarge</u>   brief   <u>expand</u>

3 sea   <u>harbour</u>   ocean   <u>pier</u>   lake

4 sturdy   <u>weak</u>   strong   healthy   <u>ill</u>

5 walk   <u>swim</u>   stride   <u>dive</u>   march

5

Find the three-letter word which can be added to the letters in capitals to make a new word. The new word will complete the sentence sensibly.

Example   The cat sprang onto the MO.   <u>USE</u>

6 The weather was W and sunny.   _____

7 He SCHED high and low for the remote control.   _____

8 I've got some nice, new PYAS to wear.   _____

9 My favourite fruit is an APRI.   _____

10 The octopus got him with its TACLES.   _____

5

7

Which one letter can be added to the front of all of these words to make new words?

	Example	_c_are	_c_at	_c_rate	_c_all

11 __late   __lease   __ony   __each

12 __right   __ig   __all   __road

13 __how   __et   __poon   __nake

14 __elt   __eal   __at   __oan

15 __hall   __eal   __mall   __nail

5

Add one letter to the word in capital letters to make a new word. The meaning of the new word is given in the clue.

Example   PLAN   simple   _plain_

16 TROT   a fish   _____

17 NOSE   the opposite of silence   _____

18 TICK   the opposite of thin   _____

19 LATE   used to put our food on   _____

20 SORT   different types of games   _____

5

Fill in the crosswords so that all the given words are included. You have been given one letter as a clue in each crossword.

21
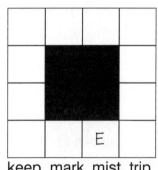
keep, mark, mist, trip

22
T

date, fire, half, hard

23
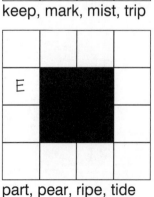
part, pear, ripe, tide

3

Fill in the missing number in each sequence.

Example   2   4   6   8   <u>10</u>

24   3   6   9   ___   15

25   12   10   8   ___   4

26   12   24   ___   48   60

27   21   32   43   ___   65

28   121   232   ___   454   565

5

These words have been written in code, but the codes are not under the right words.

TOO   OUT   TOT   TO   UP

72   722   247   46   727

Write the correct code for each word.

29 TOO _____

30 OUT _____

31 TOT _____

32 TO _____

33 UP _____

5

If a = 1, b = 2, c = 3, find the sum of:

34 a + b + c = _____

35 c + 2b = _____

36 2a + 2b = _____

3

Underline the one word which **cannot be made** from the letters of the word in capital letters.

Example   S T A T I O N E R Y   stones   tyres   ration   <u>nation</u>   noisy

37 CONSIDER   cried   nice   dear   rice   coin

38 LOWEST   low   west   flow   sew   owl

39 TEACHER   eaten   chat   ear   are   crate

40 INSIDE   den   snide   end   dine   need

4

In each line, underline the word which has its letters in alphabetical order.

41 gas   guzzle   grunt   got

42 apple   ant   ask   ale

43 clever   caution   care   cry

44 deal   dint   dream   drink

45 flow   flea   frank   frog

5

Now go to the Progress Chart to record your score!   Total   45

Paper 4

Find and underline the two words which need to change places for each sentence to make sense.

Example   She went to <u>letter</u> the <u>write</u>.

1 The tail wagged her dog when she saw the treat.

2 My sister told my mother to finish her homework.

3 I like to read a bed before book.

4 At my birthday cake we ate ice cream and party.

5 My mum takes the office to her bus.

5

Underline two words, one from each group, that go together to form a new word. The word in the first group always comes first.

Example   (hand, <u>green</u>, for)   (light, <u>house</u>, sure)

6 (wood, light, sea)   (day, tree, weed)

7 (earth, glass, sand)   (sun, castle, rain)

8 (well, work, pail)   (shop, cut, know)

9 (foot, glove, hand)   (knee, head, shake)

10 (under, over, through)   (sky, place, water)

5

Fill in the crosswords so that all the given words are included. You have been given one letter as a clue in each crossword.

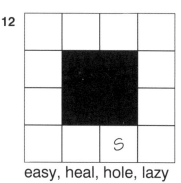

11
A	■	■	
	■	■	

keen, park, port, torn

12
	■	■	
	■	■	
		S	

easy, heal, hole, lazy

⬭ 2

Underline one word in the brackets which is most opposite in meaning to the word in capitals.

Example   WIDE   (broad   vague   long   <u>narrow</u>   motorway)

13 HEALTHY   (good   doctor   hospital   ill   patient)

14 TEACHER   (school   pupil   lesson   term   tutor)

15 FRIEND   (pal   mate   foe   ally   neighbour)

16 MANY   (more   lots   few   crowd   half)

17 WHOLE   (entire   part   some   complete   full)

⬭ 5

Find the three-letter word which can be added to the letters in capitals to make a new word. The new word will complete the sentence sensibly.

Example   The cat sprang onto the MO.   U̲S̲E̲

18 A baby is an INT.   _____

19 A baby goes out in a P.   _____

20 A baby CLS on the floor.   _____

21 A baby plays with a TLE.   _____

22 A baby sits in a HIGHCH.   _____

⬭ 5

Add one letter to the word in capital letters to make a new word. The meaning of the new word is given in the clue.

Example   PLAN   simple   _plain_

23 WAS   an insect   _____

24 HOP   to expect the best   _____

25 LOW   the opposite of fast   _____

26 HAT   to stop   _____

27 RAN   it pours   _____

Complete the following expressions by underlining the missing word.

Example   Frog is to tadpole as swan is to (duckling, baby, cygnet).

28 Sun is to sunk as pin is to (sink, pin, pan, pink).

29 Fat is to feat as mat is to (mate, team, fate, meat).

30 Bed is to bead as led is to (late, lead, deal, lane).

31 Fin is to find as bin is to (bend, bind, bond, band).

32 Cot is to coat as got is to (good, hot, goat, heat).

33 Ail is to bail as ill is to (sill, will, kill, bill).

Write each word backwards and then list them in reverse alphabetical order.

34   boy   but   why   she   sty

_____   _____   _____   _____   _____

These words have been written in code, but the codes are not under the right words.

BE   BEG   BIN   BEGIN   BEE

244   24538   24   245   238

Write the correct code for each word.

35 BE   36 BEG   37 BIN   38 BEE   39 BEGIN

_____   _____   _____   _____   _____

If a = 3, b = 2, d = 6, e = 8, f = 10, find the value of:

40 $2f - 2a = $ ___

41 $2e - 2b = $ ___

2

Sue and Omar wear yellow tops.

Lee and Omar wear green trousers.

Sue and Jess wear brown trousers.

Jess and Lee wear red tops.

Who wears:

42 a yellow top and brown trousers? _____

43 a red top and green trousers? _____

44 a yellow top and green trousers? _____

45 a red top and brown trousers? _____

4

Now go to the Progress Chart to record your score!   Total   45

Paper 5

Which one letter can be added to the front of all of these words to make new words.

Example   care   cat   crate   call

1 ___arm   ___and   ___as   ___ollow

2 ___old   ___hill   ___loud   ___an

3 ___read   ___ream   ___ark   ___ome

4 ___and   ___right   ___ear   ___each

5 ___rim   ___ower   ___ride   ___lant

5

The train was due in at 10:50. It was 10 minutes late.

6 When did it arrive? _____

I left home at 18:15. It took me 20 minutes to walk to the cinema.

7 When did I get there? _____

A pudding takes 50 minutes to cook. I want it to be ready for 13:00.

8 When must I put it into the oven? _____ 3

If these words were placed in alphabetical order, which word would come first?

9 Monday Thursday Wednesday Friday Tuesday _____

10 May January March February April _____

11 giraffe elephant mouse horse dog _____

12 plane helicopter kite balloon rocket _____ 4

Underline one word in the brackets which is most opposite in meaning to the word in capitals.

Example WIDE (broad vague long <u>narrow</u> motorway)

13 WARM (hot cold icy sun fine)

14 BLACK (dark brown white sooty coal)

15 HIDE (lost last find skin search)

16 MORE (less many few lots plenty)

17 FIRST (top bottom side last enough) 5

Underline two words which are made from the same letters.

Example TAP PET <u>TEA</u> POT <u>EAT</u>

18 MAUL PART MAKE TRAM TRAP

19 AGES ALES APES SAGE SAND

20 LIMP LEAP PEEP PEAL PEARL

21 WARN WARM WARD WARP DRAW

22 LATE LINT TALE TILE FILE 5

Remove one letter from the word in capitals to leave a new word. The meaning of the new word is given in the clue.

Example   A U N T   an insect   <u>ant</u>

23 ROAD   a stick   _____

24 PINT   something we use when sewing   _____

25 TINT   a metal   _____

26 CODE   a type of fish   _____

27 HARM   part of our body   _____   ⬤ 5

Underline the number that completes each sequence.

28 4 is to 16 as 16 is to (72, 64, 60)

29 3 is to 12 as 12 is to (24, 36, 48)

30 32 is to 16 as 16 is to (4, 8, 12)

31 22 is to 11 as 24 is to (11, 12, 14)

32 100 is to 50 as 90 is to (55, 40, 45)   ⬤ 5

These words have been written in code, but the codes are not under the right words.

STOW	SLOW	STEW	LOW	STOLE
9687	96418	9147	9647	147

Write the correct code for each word.

33 STOW   34 SLOW   35 STEW   36 LOW   37 STOLE   ⬤ 5

_____   _____   _____   _____   _____

Underline the word in the brackets which goes best with the words given outside the brackets.

Example   word, paragraph, sentence   (pen, cap, <u>letter</u>, top, stop)

38 bed, bunk, mattress   (drawer, cold, warm, film, pillow)

39 car, lorry, bicycle   (train, road, bus, speed, track)

40 sheep, cows, chickens   (farm, tractor, shed, pigs, bird)

(15)

41 money, cash, notes   (cheque, bank, lesson, coins, save)

42 mat, tiles, carpet   (curtains, rug, kitchen, sofa, stairs)

Fill in the crosswords so that all the given words are included. You have been given one letter as a clue in each crossword.

43

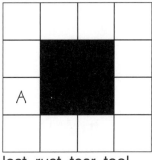

lost, rust, tear, tool

44

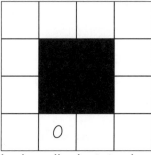

leak, sail, shot, took

45

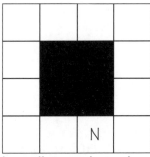

less, list, seek, tank

Now go to the Progress Chart to record your score!   Total   45

Paper 6

Underline one word in the brackets which is most opposite in meaning to the word in capital letters.

    Example   WIDE   (broad   vague   long   <u>narrow</u>   motorway)

  1 SHORT   (length   long   low   metre   up)

  2 UP   (saw   went   go   down   tall)

  3 YOUNG   (old   clothes   pretty   dress   new)

  4 EVEN   (smooth   plain   old   odd   straight)

  5 FASTEN   (collar   fix   loosen   tie   bind)

Fill in the crosswords so that all the given words are included. You have been given one letter as a clue in each crossword.

6

R

even, idle, iron, noon

7

E

told, nail, want, went

8

T

bare, hare, bath, rear

3

In each line one word has been muddled up. Rearrange the letters so it fits in with the others.

Example   fly   spider   moth   gnat   <u>tan</u>   <u>ant</u>

9   dove   lark   wren   tit   low   _____

10   rain   owns   mist   hail   fog   _____

11   lump   pear   date   lime   apple   _____

12   cake   pork   wets   buns   ham   _____

13   goat   lamb   deer   loaf   calf   _____

5

Change the first word into the last word by changing one letter at a time and making a new, different word in the middle.

Example   C A S E   <u>C A S H</u>   L A S H

14   LAND   _____   PAID

15   PLAN   _____   CLAP

16   PAID   _____   HAIL

17 WORD _____ TOLD

18 SILK _____ TILL

5

Change the first word of the third pair in the same way as the other pairs to give a new word.

Example bind, hind   bare, hare   but, hut

19 rest, test   road, toad   rent, _____

20 chip, hip   park, ark   mice, _____

21 tear, tar   fear, far   bear, _____

22 bet, beat   set, seat   met, _____

23 and, band   old, bold   all, _____

5

In each line, underline the word which has its letters in alphabetical order.

24 ACE   DEBT   EIGHT   MORE

25 FEW   LIPS   MOST   ROOM

2

Find the three-letter word which can be added to the letters in capitals to make a new word. The new word will complete the sentence sensibly.

Example The cat sprang onto the MO.   USE

26 A donkey BS.   _____

27 A cock CS.   _____

28 A lion RS.   _____

29 A dog BS.   _____

30 A pig GTS.   _____

5

If the code for LATHER is ABCDEF, what are the codes for the following words?

31 REAL _____   32 LATE _____   33 HEAL _____

What do these codes stand for?

34 DEF _____   35 CEECD _____

5

The day after tomorrow is Friday.

36 What was the day before yesterday? _____

If Joshua was a year older he would be three times as old as his brother. His brother is 4.

37 How old is Joshua? _____

I have 20p more than Gita who has 40p less than Mike. Mike has £1.20.

38 How much does Gita have? _____

39 How much do I have? _____   4

Underline the two words which are the odd ones out in the following groups of words.

    Example   black   <u>king</u> purple green <u>house</u>

40 banana   pear   yellow   purple   apple

41 finger   ring   knee   hat   ear

42 rose   daffodil   daisy   leaf   stem

43 tennis   bat   ball   rugby   swimming   4

Fill in the crosswords so that all the given words are included. You have been given one letter as a clue in each crossword.

44

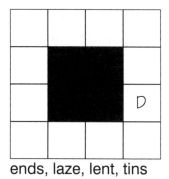

ends, laze, lent, tins

45

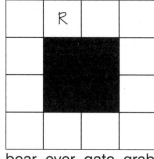

bear, ever, gate, grab   2

Paper 7

Look at these groups of words.

Group A Animals   Group B Colours   Group C Birds

Choose the correct group for each of the words below. Write in the letter.

1 purple __   2 ferret __   3 swan __   4 rabbit __   5 wren __   **5**

Underline the pair of words most opposite in meaning.

	Example	cup, mug	coffee, milk	hot, cold
6	yes, no		tall, fat	roam, wander
7	happy, glad		teach, learn	blue, sea
8	sorry, cry		quick, run	less, more
9	work, play		high, jump	bright, shining
10	rain, puddle		cat, food	wet, dry

5

Underline the one word which **cannot be made** from the letters of the word in capital letters.

	Example	S T A T I O N E R Y	stone	tyres	ration	nation	noisy
11	PROFIT	for	toe	top	rot	fit
12	GROWTH	who	got	hot	wet	how
13	COWARD	cod	car	over	row	crow
14	GRAPES	sap	sea	ear	art	peg
15	PATIENT	tap	pin	not	ten	net

5

Look at the first group of three words. The word in the middle has been made from the other two words. Complete the second group of three words in the same way, making a new word in the middle.

	Example	PAIN	INTO	TOOK		ALSO	SOON	ONLY
16	ALSO	SOON	ONLY		YEAR	_____	CHIN
17	GRIN	GRAB	STAB		PLUM	_____	SCAN
18	MALT	ALSO	SAGO		SMOG	_____	SEAS
19	GATE	GAME	TIME		ROPE	_____	HOSE
20	THIN	MOTH	MOON		STAB	_____	PEAL

5

20

Complete the following sentences by selecting the most sensible word from each group of words given in the brackets. Underline the words selected.

Example   The (<u>children</u>, books, foxes) carried the (houses, <u>books</u>, steps) home from the (greengrocer, <u>library</u>, factory).

21 Tom saw a (bird, walrus, rabbit) run down a (chimney, hole, pavement) and into its (drey, burrow, sleep).

22 I feel (cold, lazy, hot) so I must put on a (swim suit, jumper, sandals) then I will feel warmer.

23 The (firework, balloons, streamers) were (burst, inflated, candle) for the party.

24 Clare (wrote, played, sent) a (page, text, letter) to Anya's mobile phone.

25 They (ran, walked, swam) across the (house, class, lake) to the (mist, frog, island).

5

Remove one letter from the word in capital letters to leave a new word. The meaning of the new word is given in the clue.

Example   A U N T   an insect   <u>ant</u>

26 BLESS   fewer   _____

27 THEN   a chicken   _____

28 MEAN   male   _____

29 REED   a colour   _____

4

Fill in the crosswords so that all the given words are included. You have been given one letter as a clue in each crossword.

30
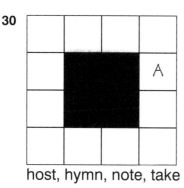
host, hymn, note, take

31
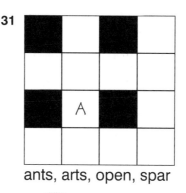
ants, arts, open, spar

2

32 If the code for SPIN is ABDE, what is the code for NIPS? _____

33 If the code for RING is CDEF, what is the code for GRIN? _____

34 If the code for SPRIG is ABCDF, what is the code for PRIG? _____

35 If the code for SEAT is 3521, what is the code for TEAS? _____

36 If the code for STEAM is 31526, what is the code for MAST? _____ ⃝ 5

Fill in the missing number or letters in each sequence.

Example   2   4   6   8   <u>10</u>

37 10   20   40   ___   160

38 28   24   20   ___   12

39 19   25   ___   37   43

40 11   ___   17   20   23

41 bb   bc   bd   ___   bf   ⃝ 5

Look at this chart.

	English	Art	Maths	Science	ICT
Girls	5	6	2	1	3
Boys	4	2	4	6	3

42 Which subject is liked by twice as many boys as girls? _____

43 Which subject is three times as popular with girls as with boys? _____

44 Which subject is most popular with boys? _____

45 Which subject was liked equally well by boys and girls? _____ ⃝ 4

Now go to the Progress Chart to record your score!   Total ⃝ 45

Paper 8

If a = 1, b = 2, c = 3, d = 4, e = 5, f = 6, find the sum of:

1 a + b + c = ___   2 d + e + f = ___

3 2a + b =   ___   4 2b + c =   ___

5 3a + 2b =   ___   6 e + f =   ___   ⃝ 6

(22)

Rearrange the muddled letters in capitals to make a proper word. The answer will complete the sentence sensibly.

Example   A BEZAR is an animal with stripes.   ZEBRA

7   Half of six is HERET.   _____

8   Sheep have a thick OLWO coat.   _____

9   Don't drop TILTRE in the street.   _____

10 The fire crew used AETRW to put out the blaze.   _____

11 The tower of the HRCCHU was floodlit.   _____   5

Complete the following sentences by selecting the most sensible word from each group of words given in the brackets. Underline the words selected.

Example   The (children, books, foxes) carried the (houses, books, steps) home from the (greengrocer, library, factory).

12 It was (hot, cold, freezing) and she (hated, wanted, disliked) a (pie, hot soup, cold drink) to cool her down.

13 Where is my (shoe, coat, book)? I left it (hiding, running, hanging) in the (shelf, kitchen, cupboard).

14 The (king, soldier, dog) sat in his (car, basket, larder) and (swam, growled, argued).   3

Underline the pair of words most opposite in meaning.

Example   cup, mug   coffee, milk   hot, cold

15 cross, happy   sad, sorry   start, begin

16 neat, tidy   hard, soft   soap, water

17 eat, drink   boil, water   loud, noisy

18 cold, cool   shut, open   oil, tank

19 paper, pencil   pen, write   cry, laugh   5

Look at the first group of three words. The word in the middle has been made from the other two words. Complete the second group of three words in the same way, making a new word in the middle.

Example   PAIN INTO TOOK   ALSO SOON ONLY

20 RASH   RAIN   GRIN   CLAN   _____   SLIP

21 POST   STAR   ARMY   POSH   _____   INTO

23

22	CRAG	CREW	EWES	BLUE	_____	ABLE
23	CHAT	CHIN	RAIN	SLAT	_____	SHAM
24	EVEN	VERY	EERY	PLOT	_____	BOOT

○ 5

Underline the two words which are the odd ones out in the following groups of words.

Example black <u>king</u> purple green <u>house</u>

25	cot	sleep	cradle	sing	bed
26	cat	little	water	minute	small
27	road	long	tall	street	fat
28	coat	new	dress	pretty	suit
29	sorry	pleased	happy	glad	old

○ 5

Fill in the missing letters. The alphabet has been written out to help you.

A B C D E F G H I J K L M N O P Q R S T U V W X Y Z

Example A B is to C D as P Q is to <u>R S</u>

30 A30 is to B29 as C28 is to _____

31 D20 is to E19 as F18 is to _____

32 100A is to 95B as 90C is to _____

33 A2 is to B3 as C4 is to _____

34 F1 is to E2 as D3 is to _____

○ 5

Find and underline the two words which need to change places for each sentence to make sense.

Example She went to <u>letter</u> the <u>write</u>.

35 The drive was parked in the car.

36 We went to holiday for our Scotland.

37 I have to eat my pudding before I can have supper.

38 The shop on my road sweets sells.

39 We are moving our house and selling to Wales.

○ 5

If the code for SECOND is ABCDEF, what are the codes for the following words?

40 ONE _____   41 CODE _____   42 ONCE _____

What do these codes stand for?

43 FDEB _____   44 FDAB _____   45 ABEF _____   ◯ 6

Now go to the Progress Chart to record your score!   Total ◯ 45

Paper 9

Underline the pair of words most similar in meaning.

Example   come, go   roam, wander   fear, fare

1 fade, tint   blank, empty   hinder, go

2 cut, slit   hit, miss   less, more

3 dry, fine   rich, poor   tea, coffee

4 add, subtract   hole, gap   red, colour

5 tired, weary   hot, cold   forgot, remember   ◯ 5

Find the three-letter word which can be added to the letters in capitals to make a new word. The new word will complete the sentence sensibly.

Example   The cat sprang onto the MO.   USE

6 The police will FOL the criminal.   _____

7 A DON is sometimes called an ass.   _____

8 Time to stop for a DR of water.   _____

9 He was pleased to go home from HOSAL.   _____

10 You need a BET to carry your shopping in. _____   ◯ 5

Find the letter which will end the first word and start the second word.

Example   peac (h) ome

11 gat (__) nds   12 non (__) ars   13 min (__) ust

14 ben (__) rim   15 als (__) dds   ◯ 5

25

Look at the first group of three words. The word in the middle has been made from the other two words. Complete the second group of three words in the same way, making a new word in the middle.

Example   PAIN INTO TOOK   ALSO <u>SOON</u> ONLY

16 CLAN   CLOP   STOP   RATS   _____   FISH

17 BAND   BARK   DARK   SLIP   _____   GROW

18 FISH   SHOE   WOES   FAST   _____   TOWN

19 SALT   ALSO   SOOT   PART   _____   CHOP

20 BUSH   BUNK   PINK   STEP   _____   SHOP   **5**

Complete the following sentences by selecting the most sensible word from each group of words given in the brackets. Underline the words selected.

Example   The (<u>children</u>, books, foxes) carried the (houses, <u>books</u>, steps) home from the (greengrocer, <u>library</u>, factory).

21 She spent a (lot, little, some) of money on all the things she had to (buy, sell, gather) for the big (party, card, mess).

22 The (dog, cow, rabbit) barked furiously at the (burglars, robbing, scare).

23 Tola (buy, bought, bring) her brother a DVD as a (present, surprised, gifts).

24 Don't (run, walk, stand)! You'll (stop, wait, trip) and hurt your (book, friend, knee).

25 The cinema was (dry, packed, fill) for the premiere of the (pictures, movie, showing).   **5**

If the code for WONDER is 324165, what are the codes for the following words?

26 END _____   27 DEW _____

What do these codes stand for?

28 324 _____   29 3564 _____   30 246 _____   **5**

If $a = 1$, $b = 2$, $c = 3$, $d = 4$, $e = 5$, find the sum of:

31 $c + d + b =$ __   32 $2a + 2 =$ __   33 $2c + 2d =$ __   **3**

It takes 1 hour 30 minutes to do the journey. Fill in the missing times.

34-37

Southby (depart)	Eastby (arrive)
_____	12:00
14:30	_____
16:10	_____
_____	18:30

4

If the letters in the following words are arranged in alphabetical order, which letter comes in the middle?

38 FAIRY _____   **39** PLACE _____

40 LIGHT _____   **41** TEACH _____

4

Worzles and Dingbats like to eat leaves and shoots.

Sninks and Dingbats like snails and slugs.

Worzles and Wigglers like weeds and grass.

Wigglers and Sninks like flies and berries.

42 Who likes berries but not weeds? _____

43 Who likes leaves, shoots and slugs? _____

44 Who likes snails and flies? _____

45 Who likes weeds, grass, flies and berries? _____

4

Now go to the Progress Chart to record your score!   Total   45

Paper 10

Underline the two words which are the odd ones out in the following groups of words.

Example   black   <u>king</u>   purple   green   <u>house</u>

1 child   wash   clean   parent   bath

2 circle   newspaper   ring   hoop   comic

3	grey	yellow	apple	blue	cherry
4	jeans	turban	white	brown	sweater
5	bench	ball	seat	chair	bat

5

Find the three-letter word which can be added to the letters in capitals to make a new word. The new word will complete the sentence sensibly.

Example   The cat sprang onto the MO.   U̲S̲E̲

6 The CH he sat on was hard.   _____

7 The CSE of the river was long and winding.   _____

8 The show INS at eight.   _____

9 At the start of the play the ORS appeared on the stage.   _____

10 The BN dog ran wildly after the ball.   _____

5

Find the letter which will end the first word and start the second word.

Example   peac (h̲) ome

11 lan (___) are   12 fea (___) ule

13 gon (___) ver   14 sto (___) ond

15 cla (___) hite

5

These words have been written in code, but the codes are not under the right words.

AT	THE	CHAT	HAT	ACT
2315	15	125	534	315

Write the correct code for each word.

16 AT   17 THE   18 CHAT

_____   _____   _____

19 HAT   20 ACT

_____   _____

5

21 four   fork   fire   fall   feel

If these words were placed in alphabetical order, which word would come fourth?

_____

22 If the letters in the following word are arranged in alphabetical order, which letter comes in the middle?

CHASE _____

2

Complete the following sentences by selecting the most sensible word from each group of words given in the brackets. Underline the words selected.

Example   The (children, books, foxes) carried the (houses, books, steps) home from the (greengrocer, library, factory).

23 Mai took her (spoon, spade, hoe) to the (garden, beach, park) to build a (bridge, castle, palace).

24 The workman (knocked, fixed, tied) the (string, pipe, paper) in the bathroom.

25 No one (heard, wanted, bought) the (washing, burglar, road) enter the (kennel, fridge, house).

26 Can you (wait, hinder, help) me (empty, lift, buy) this box onto the (lawn, table, dog)?

27 The (monster, policeman, owl) (hooted, whispered, sang) in the (cupboard, hall, wood).

5

Which one letter can be added to the front of all these words to make new words?

Example   care   cat   crate   call

28 __hale   __rap   __in   __art

29 __lame   __right   __one   __urn

30 __lint   __ray   __rank   __lea

31 __pen   __at   __pal   __range

32 __lip   __limb   __heat   __harm

5

Look at the first group of three words. The word in the middle has been made from the other two words. Complete the second group of three words in the same way, making a new word in the middle of the group.

Example   PAIN   INTO   TOOK   ALSO   S<u>OO</u>N   ONLY

33 VEST   VEIN   PAIN   SOME   _____   TART

34 HARP   PART   PORT   GULP   _____   BARK

35 MASH   SHIP   TRIP   FIST   _____   GRAB

36 SELL   SEAT   BEAT   HOME   _____   RIPE

37 MARK   ARMS   HEMS   PEAL   _____   BUSY   ⬭ 5

Remove one letter from the word in capital letters to leave a new word. The meaning of the new word is given in the clue.

Example   A U N T   an insect   <u>ant</u>

38 CLOUD   not quiet   _____

39 CLUB   a baby bear   _____

40 SHINE   part of the leg   _____

41 LIFE   a fib   _____

42 PANT   used for cooking   _____   ⬭ 5

43–45 In each list of words, the letters of one word have been jumbled up. Underline it and write it correctly.

FURNITURE   PARTS OF THE BODY   ANIMALS

   piano   slip   mare

   tools   nose   frog

   table   eyes   toga

   _____   _____   _____   ⬭ 3

Fill in the crosswords so that all the given words are included. You have been given one letter as a clue in each crossword.

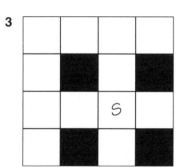

1

ever, done, opal, late

2

hats, need, tame, used

3

café, cart, fish, rush

3

Complete the following sentences by selecting the most sensible word from each group of words given in the brackets. Underline the words selected.

Example   The (children, books, foxes) carried the (houses, books, steps) home from the (greengrocer, library, factory).

4 The old lady (smiled, yawned, laughed) because she was (tired, worried, ill) and wanted to go to (hospital, bed, play).

5 The (bike, ship, bed) (fell, swerved, ran) across the (pond, road, door).

6 He carefully (waited, cooked, climbed) through the (roof, garden, window) into the (zoo, kennel, castle).

7 She turned on the (lights, curtains, towels) as it was getting (light, dark, sunny).

8 Alex (hum, danced, clap) to the (rhythm, rhyme, tone) of the music.

5

Change one word so that the sentence makes sense. Underline the word you are taking out and write your new word on the line.

Example   I waited in line to buy a <u>book</u> to see the film.   *ticket*

9   I had a toothache so my mother took me to the hairdresser.   _____

10   The swimming cage in my town has two diving boards.   _____

11   When I asked my mum what a word meant she told me to look it up in the newspaper.   _____

12   For lunch I like a cheese sandwich on brown rice and an apple.   _____

13   My birthday candle this year is going to be chocolate sponge.   _____   **5**

If the code for PARENT is ACEGIK, what are the codes for the following words?

14   TREAT _____   15   TEAR _____

16   PAN _____   17   NEAT _____

What do these codes stand for?

18   KECA _____   19   EGCA _____   20   ACEK _____   **7**

Change the first word of the third pair in the same way as the other pairs to give a new word.

Example   bind, hind   bare, hare   but, <u>hut</u>

21   light, might   line, mine   list,   _____

22   hair, air   hand, and   ball,   _____

23   beach, reach   best, rest   bake,   _____

24   oil, boil   old, bold   oat,   _____   **4**

Underline the pair of words most similar in meaning.

Example   come, go   <u>roam, wander</u>   fear, fare

25   help, hinder   hate, horrid   burden, load

26   kind, thoughtful   come, go   top, hill

27   low, slight   expect, hope   come, depart

28   little, small   fly, down   top, bottom

29   last, ever   one, once   hide, conceal   **5**

Find the three-letter word which can be added to the letters in capitals to make a new word. The new word will complete the sentence sensibly.

Example The cat sprang onto the MO. <u>USE</u>

30 We keep the mower in the garden D. _____

31 The flowers are a bright OGE colour. _____

32 She peeled the apple and composted the S. _____

33 Some PS of the book were torn. _____

34 I like the yolk but not the WE of egg. _____

5

Find the letter which will end the first word and start the second word.

Example peac (<u>h</u>) o m e

35 lon (__) ggs

36 bat (__) orn

37 mar (__) nit

38 pan (__) lse

39 mar (__) els

5

Find a word that can be put in front of each of the following words to make new, compound words.

Example CAST   FALL   WARD   POUR   <u>DOWN</u>

40	PORT	BAG	SHIP	CRAFT	_____
41	CAUSE	HIND	NEATH	COME	_____
42	SIDE	SHELL	GULL	BED	_____
43	CASTLE	PIT	STORM	PAPER	_____
44	SIDE	STRETCH	SHINE	RIGHT	_____
45	SIDE	CREASE	DOOR	LAND	_____

6

Now go to the Progress Chart to record your score!   Total   45

33

Paper 12

1–5 Look at these groups of words.

Group A Tools   Group B Musical instruments
Group C Sports or games   Group D Vegetables

Choose the correct group for each of the words below. Write in the letter.

cricket __   peas __   axe __   drum __   saw __

guitar __   potatoes __   hammer __   piano __   football __   ⭕ 5

Find the letter which will end the first word and start the second word.

Example   peac (h) ome

6 blo (__) ish   **7** pas (__) pin   **8** sho (__) ind

9 mus (__) idy   **10** puf (__) eed   ⭕ 5

Underline two words, one from each group, that go together to form a new word. The word in the first group always comes first.

Example   (hand, <u>green</u>, for)   (light, <u>house</u>, sure)

11 (in, of, out)   (fit, ill, well)

12 (was, be, do)   (front, side, back)

13 (say, fare, end)   (ill, gone, well)

14 (before, when, after)   (come, wards, wet)

15 (check, pencil, pen)   (down, side, out)   ⭕ 5

Complete the following expressions by underlining the missing word.

Example   Frog is to tadpole as swan is to (duckling, baby, <u>cygnet</u>).

16 Aunt is to uncle as girl is to (boy, cousin, son).

17 Pupils are to teachers as patients are to (surgery, doctors, accident).

18 Dog is to puppy as sheep is to (ram, lamb, cow).

19 Crowd is to people as flock is to (sheep, pigs, cows).

20 Pig is to sty as rabbit is to (drey, burrow, nest).   ⭕ 5

Fill in the crosswords so that all the given words are included. You have been given one letter as a clue in each crossword.

21

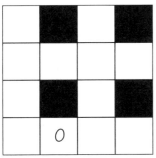

gone, news, snag, swan

22

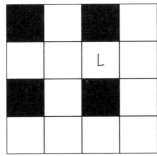

adds, apes, held, reap

23

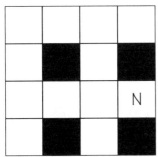

cast, chew, even, shed

24 If the first five letters of the alphabet were removed, which would be the second letter of those left? Circle the correct letter.

E   H   G   F

25 How many letters would there be in this alphabet? Circle the correct number.

20   21   22

26 Which month of the year begins with the sixth letter of the usual alphabet? _____

27 Which month of the year begins with the fourth letter? _____

If the code for STRAW is + − × ÷ @, what are the codes for the following words?

28 WAS _____   29 RAW _____   30 TAR _____

What do these codes stand for?

31 @ ÷ × _____   32 + − ÷ × _____

33–35 Mr Young was 25 when Joshua was born. Complete the table.

Mr Young's age	27		35
Joshua's age		5	

Complete the following sentences by selecting the most sensible word from each group of words given in the brackets. Underline the words selected.

Example The (children, books, foxes) carried the (houses, books, steps) home from the (greengrocer, library, factory).

36 The (race, film, job) started when the (teacher, doctor, baker) blew her (crown, pencil, whistle).

37 My mum feeds the (birds, fish, cats) each morning by putting some (jam, seed, cake) out in the (car, bin, garden).

38 In our garden we have some (swings, rocks, flowers) in a (cup, pot, dish) that sit near the back (lake, road, door).

39 Jenny set the (chair, table, television) for supper by laying out the (books, pots, forks) and (pans, knives, apples).

40 The noise of the (bikes, trees, cars) as people go to (work, sleep, play) in the (morning, holiday, sun) wakes me.

Find and underline the two words which need to change places for each sentence to make sense.

Example She went to <u>letter</u> the <u>write</u>.

41 It is too outside to go cold today.

42 The fruit apple was made with grapes, pear and salad.

43 My aunt and uncle come and spend every holiday Christmas with us.

44 The police officer told the man to move his road because it was blocking the car.

45 Sometimes when I look out of my moon at night I can see the window.

Fill in the crosswords so that all the given words are included. You have been given one letter as a clue in each crossword.

1

calm, peas, spit, time

2

also, hero, tail, tale

3

gate, girl, rude, tidy

3

Underline the pair of words most similar in meaning.

Example come, go <u>roam, wander</u> fear, fare

4 unhappy, sad   many, few   speak, listen

5 accept, refuse   divide, add   sharp, pointed

6 buy, sell   throw, catch   loud, noisy

7 cheap, inexpensive   generous, mean   rough, smooth

8 feeble, strong   give, take   terror, fear

5

Underline one word in the brackets which is most opposite in meaning to the word in capitals.

Example WIDE (broad vague long <u>narrow</u> motorway)

9 CHEERFUL   (happy pleased sad joyful thoughtful)

10 EAT   (meals starve hungry food dine)

11	MOVING	(jump still run skip slow)
12	CLEAN	(tint washed dirty dyed spill)
13	HELP	(aid assist hinder flop earn)

If the letters in the following words are arranged in alphabetical order, which letter comes in the middle?

14 POUND   _____

15 TRAIN   _____

16 READS   _____

17 AFTER   _____

Remove one letter from the word in capital letters to leave a new word. The meaning of the new word is given in the clue.

Example   A U N T an insect *ant*

18	DREAR	at the back	_____
19	SHORE	painful	_____
20	PLATE	opposite of early	_____
21	STALE	a story	_____
22	SINGE	make a tune with the voice	_____
23	PRIDE	to go on horseback	_____

If the code for SEASON is 135146, what are the codes for the following words?

24 NOSE _____   25 SANE _____   26 ONE _____

What do these codes stand for?

27 6446 _____   28 1446 _____

The pegs on one side of a cloakroom are numbered 1 to 20. On the other side they are numbered 21 to 40. 1 is opposite 21.

29 What number peg is opposite 8?   __

30 What number peg is opposite 14?   __

31 What number peg is opposite 39?   __

Underline the one word which **cannot be made** from the letters of the word in capital letters.

Example	S T A T I O N E R Y	stone	tyres	ration	<u>nation</u>	noisy
32 FLOWER	low	few	red	row	fro	
33 WANDER	and	dear	draw	need	read	
34 CURATE	eat	ate	rot	car	care	
35 MEANING	nine	man	men	none	mane	
36 FASTEN	east	sat	neat	fate	star	

5

Find a word that can be put in front of each of the following words to make new, compound words.

Example	CAST	FALL	WARD	POUR	<u>DOWN</u>
37 PIN	NET	SLIDE	DRYER	_____	
38 GO	HAND	MINE	RATE	_____	
39 MATE	YARD	OWNER	SHAPE	_____	
40 ROAR	SET	RIGHT	WARD	_____	
41 WHEEL	LOAD	RIDGE	HORSE	_____	

5

Houses 1 and 2 have green doors.

Houses 2 and 3 have brown windows.

Houses 1 and 4 have blue windows.

Houses 4 and 3 have red doors.

Which house has:

42 a green door and blue windows?   _____

43 a red door and brown windows?   _____

44 a green door and brown windows?   _____

45 a red door and blue windows?   _____

4

Paper 14

Rearrange the muddled letters in capitals to make proper words. They are all colours.

1 KPIN _____

2 YREG _____

3 YVAN _____

4 AEUVM _____

5 NORWB _____

5

Underline two words, one from each group, that go together to form a new word. The word in the first group always comes first.

Example   (hand, green, for)   (light, house, sure)

6 (old, hot, white)   (paper, plate, petal)

7 (rain, snow, wet)   (bow, arch, building)

8 (blood, tooth, pain)   (hurt, sore, ache)

9 (big, leg, foot)   (ball, park, shoe)

10 (fire, water, sea)   (switch, alarm, place)

5

Add one letter to the word in capital letters to make a new word. The meaning of the new word is given in the clue.

Example   PLAN   simple   _plain_

11 MIST   to be damp   _____

12 LOWER   grows in the garden   _____

13 FONT   opposite of back   _____

14 ROTS   a horse does this   _____

15 ROUND   land   _____

5

Underline the two words, one from each group, which are the most opposite in meaning.

Exam   (dawn, early, wake)   (late, stop, sunrise)

16 (go, back, front)   (here, for, come)

17 (moon, night, dark)   (day, shadow, dawn)

18 (full, small, big)   (over, tiny, empty)

40

19 (big, height, tall)   (large, short, huge)

20 (play, lazy, good)   (hard, cross, work)

5

Fill in the crosswords so that all the given words are included. You have been given one letter as a clue in each crossword.

21

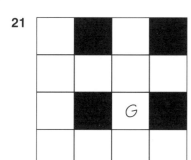

asks, sago, seat, spot

22

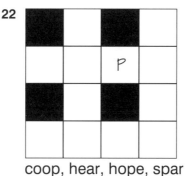

coop, hear, hope, spar

23

cart, chip, iron, root

3

Give the missing numbers and letters in the following sequences. The alphabet has been written out to help you.

A B C D E F G H I J K L M N O P Q R S T U V W X Y Z

	Example	CQ	DQ	EP	FP	*GO*
24	AE	BF	—	DH	EI	
25	4D	5E	—	7G	8H	
26	DB	EC	—	GE	HF	
27	76	65	—	43	32	
28	29	38	—	56	65	

5

If the code for MASTER is + − × ÷ % @, what are the codes for the following words?

29 TEAM _____   **30** MET _____   **31** SET _____

What do these codes stand for?

32 $+ - \times \div$ _____   **33** $- @ + \times$ _____

If a = 2, b = 3, c = 4, d = 5, e = 6, f = 7, g = 8, h = 9, find the sum of these questions. Give your answers as letters.

34	b a	**35**	b c	**36**	c c
	+ a c		+ a b		+ a b
	_____		_____		_____

Some children do a paper round.

Mike does Wednesday and Saturday. He sometimes does Monday as well.

Sally does Monday and Thursday. She never helps on Saturday.

Annie does Monday and Wednesday. She sometimes helps on Thursday.

Kim does Thursday and Saturday. She sometimes helps on Wednesday.

37 How many different children might work on Wednesday? _____

38 Who usually works on Monday? _____

39 Who works on Thursday but not Monday? _____

40 Which days of the week do none of the children work?

_____

Underline the pair of words most similar in meaning.

Example   come, go   <u>roam, wander</u>   fear, fare

41 unhappy, cross   tired, exhausted   run, skip

42 crawl, walk   sit, stand   swerve, dodge

43 mean, stingy   generous, poor   give, receive

44 army, navy   sea, harbour   soldiers, troops

45 first, last   first, tenth   double, twice

Now go to the Progress Chart to record your score!   Total   45

42

Paper 15

Underline the two words which are the odd ones out in the following groups of words.

Example   black   king   purple   green   house

1   green   grass   blue   lawn   red

2   wash   friend   pal   dry   mate

3   cod   house   salmon   herring   cottage

4   plate   cheese   dish   bread   butter

5   shoe   glove   boot   hat   sandal

5

Remove one letter from the word in capital letters to leave a new word. The meaning of the new word is given in the clue.

Example   A U N T   an insect   <u>ant</u>

6   FLIGHT   not heavy   _____

7   SWING   part of a bird   _____

8   RANK   walked fast   _____

9   COAT   a pet   _____

10 HEAT   you wear it on your head   _____

5

Fill in the crosswords so that all the given words are included. You have been given one letter as a clue in each crossword.

11

heat, pony, rain, ship

12

army, fear, fete, very

43

13

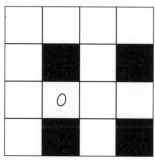

dote, late, wide, will

Change the first word of the third pair in the same way as the other pairs to give a new word.

Example   bind, hind   bare, hare   but, <u>hut</u>

14 crane, cane   plot, pot   ship, _____

15 pat, peat   wed, weed   fat, _____

16 rats, star   peek, keep   stew, _____

17 lime, mile   rite, tire   care, _____

18 sit, sat   clip, clap   flit, _____

If a = 1, b = 2, c = 3, d = 4, find the value of the following:

19 a × b × c = __   20 (b × d) − a = __   21 c × d = __

Complete the following sentences by selecting the most sensible word from each group of words given in the brackets. Underline the words selected.

Example   The (<u>children</u>, books, foxes) carried the (houses, <u>books</u>, steps) home from the (greengrocer, <u>library</u>, factory).

22 On my (day, morning, birthday) my (dog, cat, mother) makes me a special (biscuit, cake, bun).

23 The girl liked to eat (cereal, milk, chips) with her (table, soup, fish).

24 The (night, pond, moon) was (wet, slow, heavy) and (sunny, dry, windy).

25 Don't (burn, bake, eat) the (stone, king, cake). It's been (baked, poisoned, lost)!

26 Few (sheep, goats, people) have ever (seen, grazed, stolen) the ruined (hedge, pond, city).

3

5

3

5

If the code for POTION is $+ - \times \div - /$, what are the codes for the following words?

27 POOP _____ 28 INTO _____ 29 OPTION _____

What do these codes stand for?

30 $- / \div - /$ _____ 31 $\times \div / \times$ _____

Underline the word in brackets closest in meaning to the word in capitals.

Example UNHAPPY (unkind death laughter <u>sad</u> friendly)

32 CONTAIN (order help hold drop box)

33 LAST (first final try start ending)

34 WEALTHY (poor money banker rich cheque)

35 POST (wood stand box sign stake)

Underline the two words, one from each group, which are the most opposite in meaning.

Example (dawn, <u>early</u>, wake) (<u>late</u>, stop, sunrise)

36 (help, near, hope) (far, away, gone)

37 (save, money, box) (shop, keeper, spend)

38 (paint, brush, ugly) (colour, pretty, box)

39 (pat, like, friend) (unkind, sad, enemy)

40 (sound, quiet, song) (noisy, voice, sang)

Find and underline the two words which need to change places for each sentence to make sense.

Example She went to <u>letter</u> the <u>write</u>.

41 We went to the year for our holiday this sea.

42 Mike likes to go to his grandmother's school after house.

43 I forgot that had I checked a book out of the library.

44 It is important to look ways both when crossing the street.

45 I planted some seeds in the garden that I'd grown from flowers.

Complete the following sentences by selecting the most sensible word from each group of words given in the brackets. Underline the words selected.

Example The (<u>children</u>, books, foxes) carried the (houses, <u>books</u>, steps) home from the (greengrocer, <u>library</u>, factory).

1 She was very (cross, tired, glad) and said she would like to (stand, sit, run) down.

2 My older (mother, aunt, sister) went to a (school, dance, bag) with her (suitcase, dog, boyfriend).

3 She (left, gave, ate) her (car, pancake, purse) in the (pond, sea, shop).

4 Can you (speak, tell, ring) for the (ambulance, trolley, driving) from your (free, mobile, call) phone?

5 After (breakfast, lunch, supper) the (keys, bikes, moon) came up in the (day, afternoon, sky).

5

Choose the word or phrase that makes each sentence true.

Example A LIBRARY always has (posters, a carpet, books, DVDs, stairs).

6 A FOREST always has (benches, a lake, paths, flowers, trees).

7 A PIG always has (a name, a tag, a sty, a tail, spots).

8 A HUSBAND is always a (father, man, worker, driver, golfer).

9 A NURSE always works (alone, in a hospital, with patients, at night, in a city).

10 A FLOWER always has (a smell, thorns, roots, two leaves, yellow petals).

5

Underline any word which has the same letter three times.

11	December	Saturday	appears	potato
12	sparrow	trick	eleven	herring
13	individual	indeed	lesson	ironing
14	shines	eatable	release	gossip
15	necessary	alabaster	awkward	series

5

If the code for PLEASED is $+ - \times \div = \times /$, what are the codes for the following words?

16 PLEAD ＿＿＿＿＿＿   17 APPLE ＿＿＿＿＿＿   18 PALE ＿＿＿＿＿＿

What do these codes stand for?

19 $/ \div - \times$ ＿＿＿＿＿＿   20 $/ \times \times /$ ＿＿＿＿＿＿

Remove one letter from the word in capital letters to leave a new word. The meaning of the new word is given in the clue.

Example   A U N T   an insect   ~~ant~~

21 CREATE   a box   ＿＿＿＿＿＿

22 SOLID   bought by someone   ＿＿＿＿＿＿

23 WHOLE   an opening   ＿＿＿＿＿＿

24 HEARD   not soft   ＿＿＿＿＿＿

25 SUPPER   great   ＿＿＿＿＿＿

5

Underline the word in the brackets closest in meaning to the word in capitals.

Example   UNHAPPY (unkind   death   laughter   <u>sad</u>   friendly)

26 PUPILS   (teacher   parents   friends   children   neighbours)

27 FELT TIPS   (rulers   writing   books   paper   pens)

28 SOUNDS   (whispers   shouts   silence   noises   cries)

29 HOUSE   (office   shed   bungalow   castle   airport)

30 CHEST   (arm   leg   box   suitcase   crate)

5

Underline the pair of words most opposite in meaning.

Example   cup, mug   coffee, milk   <u>hot, cold</u>

31 beginning, end   unkind, stern   safe, alive

32 smooth, soft   open, closed   first, fast

33 pick, pack   high, low   short, call

34 strong, weak   up, above   eat, food

35 sleep, tired   noise, shout   quiet, loud

5

Find the three-letter word which can be added to the letters in capitals to make a new word. The new word will complete the sentence sensibly.

Example The cat sprang onto the MO. <u>USE</u>

36 My FRIS are all coming to my party. _____

37 Sixty MIES make an hour. _____

38 The building is very new and MRN. _____

39 We moved here three YS ago. _____

40 The police are offering a RED of £1000. _____

5

Underline the word in each line which uses only the first six letters of the alphabet.

41 bake   bread   feed   abbot

42 black   face   dear   bale

43 band   aces   bead   abbey

44 fade   dream   dare   bake

45 deep   beak   bill   add

5

Now go to the Progress Chart to record your score! Total **45**

Paper 17

Here is a weather chart showing hours of sunshine.

Average hours of sunshine per day

	Apr	May	Jun	July	Aug	Sept	Oct
Costa del Sol	8	10	11	11	11	9	7
Costa Brava	8	8	9	10	9	7	5
London	6	7	7	7	6	5	3

1 How many hours of sunshine should the Costa Brava have each day in July? ____

2 The Costa del Sol should get ____ hours of sunshine each day in August.

3 In July the Costa del Sol should have ____ hours of sunshine each day.

4 The Costa Brava should get ____ hours of sunshine each day in April.

5 London should get ____ hours of sunshine each day in October.

5

Underline the pair of words most opposite in meaning.

Example cup, mug   coffee, milk   <u>hot, cold</u>

6 sand, beach   heavy, light   tired, sleepy

7 run, around   write, ink   here, there

8 better, best   whisper, shout   read, write

9 late, early   fish, meat   cat, dog

10 talk, speak   date, year   glad, sad

Find the three-letter word which can be added to the letters in capitals to make a new word. The new word will complete the sentence sensibly.

Example   The cat sprang onto the MO.   <u>USE</u>

11 The runners RD each other to win.   _____

12 The PAR is a bird usually kept in a cage.   _____

13 'Do up the BUTS on your shirt!'   _____

14 Tim liked BN sugar on his cereal.   _____

15 Nishpa ENS the festival of Diwali.   _____

Find the letter which will end the first word and start the second word.

Example   peac (<u>h</u>) ome

16 han (__) eal   17 mat (__) nds   18 sal (__) wo

19 duc (__) now   20 mas (__) rack

Look at the first group of three words. The word in the middle has been made from the other two words. Complete the second group of three words in the same way, making a new word in the middle.

Example   PAIN   INTO   TOOK   ALSO   <u>SOON</u>   ONLY

21 HOME   MEAN   ANTS   SANE   _____   STAY

22 GREY   EYES   ESPY   EACH   _____   INCH

23 TEST   TEAR   ARTS   BATH   _____   SHED

24 LARK   LINK   SING   BEST   _____   NEAR

25 FIRE   FISH   SHOP   BEAR   _____   STEW

Underline the two words, one from each group, which are closest in meaning.

Example (race, shop, <u>start</u>) (finish, <u>begin</u>, end)

26 (fire, help, hinder)   (call, after, aid)

27 (ruin, match, result)   (mend, spoil, again)

28 (hate, angry, soft)   (cross, hard, fallen)

29 (talk, chat, hear)   (see, listen, cost)

30 (price, garment, till)   (shop, label, cost)

5

Rearrange the muddled words in capital letters so that each sentence makes sense.

Example There are sixty SNODCES <u>SECONDS</u> in a UTMINE <u>MINUTE</u>.

31–32 We have a DNBA _____ in our SASLC _____ .

33–34 I like playing the MURDS _____ . Mr Brown plays the AIONP _____ .

35 We make a lot of ONSIE _____ .

5

Underline the number that completes the sentence.

36 6 is to 36 as 7 is to (49, 28, 56)

37 12 is to 9 as 40 is to (12, 20, 30)

38 14 is to 21 as 21 is to (24, 28, 32)

39 4 is to 20 as 50 is to (80, 250, 100)

40 19 is to 38 as 38 is to (19, 76, 50)

5

Underline the word in brackets closest in meaning to the word in capitals.

Example UNHAPPY (unkind death laughter <u>sad</u> friendly)

41 PIP   (fruit flower seed skin flesh)

42 FROSTY   (cold snowy icy bright bitter)

43 SKID   (roll trip slide tumble brake)

44 RAISE   (upright tall lift drop collect)

45 LEAN   (tilt bend fat hungry curve)

5

Paper 18

1–5 Look at these groups of words.

Group A Kitchen things   Group B Languages

Group C Birds   Group D Animals

Choose the correct group for each of the words below. Write in the letter.

whisk ___   camel ___   Dutch ___   scales ___   gull ___

German ___   lamb ___   recipe ___   goose ___   French ___   `5`

Find the three-letter word which can be added to the letters in capitals to make a new word. The new word will complete the sentence sensibly.

Example   The cat sprang onto the MO.   <u>USE</u>

6 Have you seen the fish in the WR?   _____

7 He was wearing a stripy SF.   _____

8 You must SH the money with Nina.   _____

9 Put the HING out to dry on the line.   _____

10 No one saw him SL the money.   _____   `5`

Find the letter which will end the first word and start the second word.

Example   peac (<u>h</u>) ome

11 lan (__) own   **12** fea (__) urn   **13** gon (__) lass

14 sto (__) lace   **15** rop (__) ar   `5`

Fill in the crosswords so that all the given words are included. You have been given one letter as a clue in each crossword.

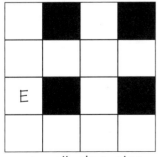

16

17

eyes, yell, slop, sips

acts, flag, food, oats   `2`

Change the first word of the third pair in the same way as the other pairs to give a new word.

Example   bind, hind   bare, hare   but, <u>hut</u>

18 and, sand   ill, sill   eat, _____

19 bet, best   cot, cost   lit, _____

20 cat, coat   bat, boat   mat, _____

21 fat, feat   mat, meat   hat, _____

22 is, this   at, that   an, _____   ⟨ 5

If the code for VEGETABLE is $+ / - / \times$ @ $ = /, what are the codes for the following words?

23 GET _____   24 BLEAT _____   25 LEAVE _____

What do these codes stand for?

26 $\times$ @ $-$ _____   27 $-$ @ $\times$ / _____   ⟨ 5

A and B wear blue jeans. C and B wear red shirts. D and A wear green shirts. C and D wear black jeans.

28 Who wore blue jeans and a red shirt?   —

29 Who wore black jeans and a green shirt?   —

30 Who wore blue jeans and a green shirt?   —

31 Who wore black jeans and a red shirt?   —   ⟨ 4

32 Underline the word which uses only the first six letters of the alphabet.

dear   cedar   bead   feast   aside   ⟨ 1

If the following letters were arranged in alphabetical order, which letter comes in the middle?

33 CRIED   _____

34 BROKE   _____

35 SWEPT   _____   ⟨ 3

52

Complete the following sentences by selecting the most sensible word from each group of words given in the brackets. Underline the words selected.

Example The (<u>children</u>, books, foxes) carried the (houses, <u>books</u>, steps) home from the (greengrocer, <u>library</u>, factory).

36 I studied my (words, letters, numbers) because we had a (running, art, spelling) test at (home, school, camp).

37 The (painter, butcher, writer) worked alone in her (car, study, desk) trying to finish her (poet, works, book).

38 When the plane (landed, swam, ran) we (waved, broke, dropped) into (silence, applause, cheers).

39 My (sister, brother, father) got a ring from her (cat, boyfriend, baby) for her (lunch, job, birthday).

40 The actress (found, lost, spent) the (second, weekend, years) learning her (lines, characters, costume).

5

Underline the pair of words most similar in meaning.

Example come, go   <u>roam, wander</u>   fear, fare

41 leave, depart	run, sit	sleep, awake
42 rough, smooth	half, whole	bitter, sour
43 messy, neat	calm, peaceful	rude, polite
44 sweep, brush	loose, tight	hungry, full
45 straight, crooked	grateful, thankful	less, more

5

Now go to the Progress Chart to record your score!   Total   **45**

Paper 19

Underline the word in brackets closest in meaning to the word in capitals.

Example UNHAPPY   (unkind   death   laughter   <u>sad</u>   friendly)

1 SIMILAR   (different   wrong   same   familiar   smile)

2 TALK   (shout   say   whisper   argue   cry)

3 ALLOW   (stop   low   ask   let   all)

4 DEAR   (sweet   light   honest   dare   beloved)

5 BEECH   (sand   sea   tree   plant   branch)   5

Find the three-letter word which can be added to the letters in capitals to make a new word. The new word will complete the sentence sensibly.

Example   The cat sprang onto the MO.   USE

6 The tennis CTS were fully booked.   _____

7 The police issued a WART for his arrest.   _____

8 My sister wears ARMDS for swimming.   _____

9 When the sun shines I can see my SOW.   _____

10 I need to SHAR my pencil.   _____   5

Find the letter which will end the first word and start the second word.

Example   peac (h) ome

11 gat (__) ase

12 min (__) act

13 zon (__) tch

14 ben (__) rim

15 als (__) dds   5

Give the missing letters or numbers in each sequence. The alphabet has been written out to help you.

A B C D E F G H I J K L M N O P Q R S T U V W X Y Z

Example   CQ   DQ   EP   FP   *GO*

16 A   D   G   J   ___   P

17 2B   4D   6F   8H   ___   12L

18 ABD   CDF   EFH   GHJ   ___   KLN

19 MAB   NBC   OCD   PDE   ___   RFG

20 9AB   8CD   7EF   6GH   ___   4KL   5

54

Fill in the crosswords so that all the given words are included. You have been given one letter as a clue in each crossword.

21
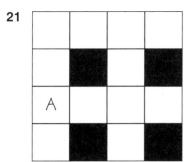
dale, leap, alas, deal

22
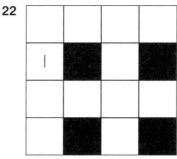
pain, into, note, pint

23
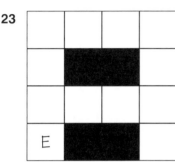
slow, site, week, type

○ 3

Rearrange the muddled letters in capitals to make a proper word. The answer will complete the sentence sensibly.

Example   A BEZAR is an animal with stripes.   ZEBRA

24 We came at last to the ALECST gate.   _____

25 Has AOEYNN seen my pen?   _____

26 The IPREAT had a bag of money and a parrot.   _____

27 We're going to the NICEAM tomorrow evening.   _____

28 Please can you do the GNIPOPSH today?   _____

○ 5

These words have been written in code, but the codes are not under the right words.

TOP	POT	TOO	TON	NOTE
6417	144	146	541	145

Write the correct code for each word.

29 TOP   30 POT   31 TOO   32 TON   33 NOTE

_____   _____   _____   _____   _____

○ 5

55

Complete the following sentences by selecting the most sensible word from each group of words given in the brackets. Underline the words selected.

> **Example** The (<u>children</u>, books, foxes) carried the (houses, <u>books</u>, steps) home from the (greengrocer, <u>library</u>, factory).

34 The (queen, king, prince) who lived in a (shed, train, castle) only wore her (hair, shoes, crown) for special occasions.

35 I set my alarm (pen, torch, clock) for seven o'clock because I wanted to be (on time, late, known) for my first day at (school, moon, tea).

36 During the (summer, winter, autumn) we sometimes get (snow, rain, clouds) which means we get to go (sledging, eating, sun bathing).

37 When I feel (well, ill, happy) my grandmother gives me some (medicine, trousers, glasses) to help me feel (sad, worse, better).

4

Remove one letter from the word in capital letters to leave a new word. The meaning of the new word is given in the clue.

> **Example** A U N T   an insect   <u>ant</u>

38 SNAP   a rest   _____

39 SPEND   to tell to go   _____

40 SPOKE   to push or jab   _____

41 SPOIL   dirt or earth   _____

42 HAUNT   a relative   _____

5

If the word DAUGHTERS is written in code as 123456789, what is the sum of these words?

43 D + A + T + E = _____

44 R + E + A + D = _____

45 T + R + E + E = _____

3

Now go to the Progress Chart to record your score! **Total** 45

56

Paper 20

Complete these questions. The alphabet has been given to help you.

A B C D E F G H I J K L M N O P Q R S T U V W X Y Z

Example   AB is to CD as PQ is to <u>RS</u>

1   A35 is to B40 as C45 is to _____

2   29A is to 31B as 33C is to _____

3   AZ is to BY as CX is to _____

4   AB is to CD as EF is to _____

5   W is to V as U is to _____

5

Fill in the missing number in each sequence.

Example   2   4   6   8   <u>10</u>

6   1   2   4   7   ___   16

7   40   36   ___   28   24   20

8   5   10   15   ___   25   30

9   24   21   ___   15   12   9

10   7   14   21   28   ___   42

5

These words have been written in code, but the codes are not under the correct words. One code is missing.

RAN	ADD	RAIN	RING	AND
4751	4275	256	266	

Write the correct code for each word.

11 RAN   12 ADD   13 RAIN   14 RING   15 AND

_____   _____   _____   _____   _____

5

If the word MARIGOLD is written in code as 12345678, what is the sum of these words?

16 G + O + L + D = _____   17 G + R + I + M = _____

18 L + A + I + R = _____

3

Underline the two words which are made from the same letters.

> **Example** TAP PET <u>TEA</u> POT <u>EAT</u>

19 INCH CHAP CHIN NICE PACK

20 CRUSH SHUSH BRUSH SHRUB BUNCH

21 RAIN NEAT NEAR EARN TENT

22 CLASP CLASS SCORE PLACE SCALP

4

Change one word so that the sentence makes sense. Underline the word you are taking out and write your new word on the line.

> **Example** I waited in line to buy a <u>book</u> to see the film. *ticket*

23 I ran out of toothpaste so couldn't brush my feet. _____

24 The pig barked to be let into the house. _____

25 'It isn't my reason that the window is broken!' _____

3

Underline the pair of words most similar in meaning.

> **Example** come, go <u>roam, wander</u> fear, fare

26 young, old   brief, short   good, bad

27 in, out   better, worse   glad, happy

28 dark, light   yell, scream   colour, plain

29 talk, speak   cold, hot   bed, time

30 read, story   see, look   eat, food

5

Find the three-letter word which can be added to the letters in capitals to make a new word. The new word will complete the sentence sensibly.

> **Example** The cat sprang onto the MO. <u>USE</u>

31 We TLED through the crowds. _____

32 The SPACES landed on the moon. _____

33 The eagle SED effortlessly. _____

34 We FOLED the path to the sea. _____

35 The player SCO a goal. _____

5

Find the letter which will end the first word and start the second word.

Example   peac (<u>h</u>) ome

36 hai (—) ean   **37** mos (—) ime

38 pai (—) rip   **39** bel (—) hen

40 cak (—) ven

(5)

Underline two words, one from each group, that go together to form a new word. The word in the first group always comes first.

Example   (hand, <u>green</u>, for)   (light, <u>house</u>, sure)

41 (birth, help, cradle)   (less, more, much)

42 (pick, slow, set)   (end, back, forward)

43 (in, smoke, match)   (fire, water, stick)

44 (dirty, mess, clean)   (time, old, age)

45 (let, come, in)   (room, doors, stairs)

(5)

Now go to the Progress Chart to record your score!   Total (45)

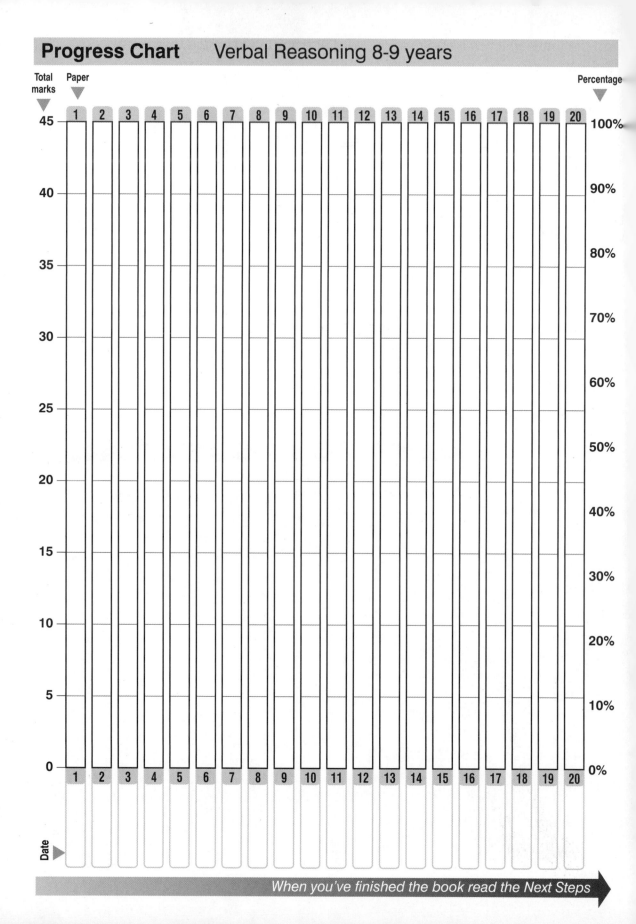

Progress Chart   Verbal Reasoning 8-9 years

Total marks

Paper

Percentage

| | 1 | 2 | 3 | 4 | 5 | 6 | 7 | 8 | 9 | 10 | 11 | 12 | 13 | 14 | 15 | 16 | 17 | 18 | 19 | 20 | |

45 — 100%

40 — 90%

35 — 80%

— 70%

30 — 60%

25 —

— 50%

20 — 40%

15 — 30%

10 — 20%

5 — 10%

0 — 0%

| 1 | 2 | 3 | 4 | 5 | 6 | 7 | 8 | 9 | 10 | 11 | 12 | 13 | 14 | 15 | 16 | 17 | 18 | 19 | 20 |

Date

When you've finished the book read the Next Steps →